SAY NO TO

ALCOHOL

Simple Tips to
Help You Cut Down
or Quit Drinking

Caroline Roope

summersdale

SAY NO TO ALCOHOL

Text by Caroline Roope

An Hachette UK Company
www.hachette.co.uk

Summersdale Publishers Ltd
Part of Octopus Publishing Group Limited
Carmelite House
50 Victoria Embankment
LONDON
EC4Y 0DZ
UK

www.summersdale.com

Printed and bound in Poland

ISBN: 978-1-80007-149-0

CONTENTS

INTRODUCTION

From a churning stomach to those feelings of regret, we all know that alcohol isn't really our friend. It lures us in, promising we can be happier, wittier and more alluring. It'll bring out the best in us – or so it says.

But the following day, in the throes of a hangover, we're left questioning our choice of bedfellow. We vow never to let a drop of alcohol pass our lips again. And yet... that's exactly what we do. Not just once, or twice, but repeatedly. Sound familiar?

You're not alone. Alcohol has been the go-to drink for numerous occasions throughout history. The ancient Greeks even had a god of wine – Dionysus – who provided them with an excuse for mass drunkenness under the guise of "worshipping". The Romans took it one step further with their own revelling deity, Bacchus, who brought the gift of inebriation to all his followers. And let's not forget that beer often quenched the thirst of our medieval ancestors, for whom drinking unsanitized water would have meant a death sentence. Thankfully, this is no longer a concern and most of us drink alcohol for the sheer pleasure of it. But therein lies the problem – it's all too easy to find a reason to drink. Bad day? Have a glass of wine. Good day? Pour yourself a pint. Celebrating? Let's open that bottle of fizz. Before you know it, it's become a habit with some really unpleasant side-effects.

Perhaps you're sick of – well – feeling sick. Or maybe you're fed up with your bank balance being depleted, with nothing to show for it but empty bottles and a fuzzy memory. Or perhaps you're considering a healthier lifestyle and know that cutting your alcohol intake is the first important step. Whatever your reasons, and whether you simply want to cut back or say no to alcohol completely, this book offers advice, tips and suggestions to help you on your way.

After all, alcohol isn't going anywhere – but you can change how you deal with it.

Gender can play a significant role in how our bodies respond to alcohol use. Studies show that women are more likely to have negative health effects from long-term drinking than men, even if a woman drinks less over a shorter period of time.

Dark liquors such as whisky are more likely to result in a severe hangover than clear liquors such as gin and vodka. Chemicals formed during the fermentation of alcohol – known as congeners – increase the severity of a hangover. A research review into hangovers, which was supported by the National Institute on Alcohol Abuse and Alcoholism, found that hangovers occurred in 33 per cent of subjects who drank bourbon (which is high in congeners), but in only 3 per cent of those who drank the same measure of vodka (which is low in congeners). As a rule of thumb, the darker a liquor, the worse you'll feel. Or, you could just say *no*...

Alcohol use is a significant risk factor for dementia. A long-term study conducted in France and published in *The Lancet* in 2018 found that in nearly 60,000 cases of early-onset dementia, 39 per cent were caused by long-term excessive consumption of alcohol and 18 per cent had an additional diagnosis of alcohol-use disorders.

The World Health Organization reports that
the harmful use of alcohol can also result in
harm to other people, such as family members,
friends, co-workers and strangers. Moreover,
the harmful use of alcohol results in a significant
health, social and economic burden on wider
society, with more than 200 diseases and injury
conditions attributed, at least in part, to its use.

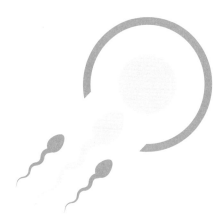

Heavy drinking can have a profound effect on fertility. The UK's Royal College of Obstetricians and Gynaecologists reports that excessive consumption of alcohol lowers testosterone levels and sperm quality and quantity in men. Not only that, it can also reduce libido and cause impotence. A study conducted in Australia also found that consuming between one and five alcoholic drinks a week can reduce a woman's chances of conceiving, and ten drinks or more decrease the likelihood of conception even further. However, the effects can be reversed by reducing alcohol intake and maintaining a healthy lifestyle.

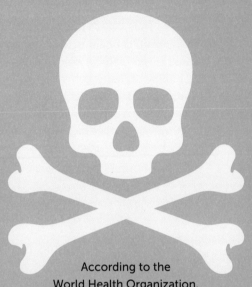

According to the
World Health Organization,
3 million deaths every year occur as a
result of the harmful use of alcohol,
representing over 5 per cent of
all deaths globally.

As well as being linked to more than 200 health conditions, alcohol is also responsible for many road traffic accidents. In the US, Canada, Australia, New Zealand, Argentina and many European countries, alcohol is a factor in around a third of all traffic deaths.

Worldwide, excessive alcohol consumption can
cause death and disability relatively early in life.
According to the World Health Organization,
in the 20–39 age group, approximately 14
per cent of all deaths can be attributed to
alcohol, including fatalities due to road traffic
crashes, violence, accidents and suicide.
Overall, 5 per cent of the global burden of
disease and injury is attributable to alcohol.

Households in Azerbaijan typically spend the least on alcohol — just 0.5 per cent of their total household expenditure. Households in the Republic of Ireland spend the most at 7.7 per cent. Just think what you could be spending that money on instead...

A long-term study published in *The Lancet* in 2019 reported that our global alcohol intake has increased by 70 per cent in the past 30 years. This soaring rate is forecast to continue to 2030, increasing the global burden of disease, injuries and death.

WHAT'S SO BAD ABOUT ALCOHOL?

Anyone who has suffered the effects of a hangover will confirm that too much alcohol is bad for you. In the short term, alcohol makes us feel lethargic, nauseous and gives us a pounding headache. In the long term, it can cause a variety of undesirable effects ranging from high blood pressure to cancer and liver disease. And that's just the physical effects. Alcohol also negatively impacts on our relationships, mental health, sleep, fertility, concentration and even our eyesight. With such a dire prognosis, going alcohol-free suddenly seems much less of a hardship! This chapter aims to help you decide whether alcohol is becoming less of a friend and more of a foe.

FRIEND, OR FOE?

While it isn't all bad news, the problems alcohol can cause – in both the short and long term – far outweigh any benefits. Let's look at the evidence:

Friend

- In small quantities, it can help us to relax.
- Drinking in moderation is a pleasant and sociable way to pass the time.
- It's a nice treat on a special occasion.

Foe

- It can cause vomiting, diarrhoea and stomach ulcers.
- It can impair judgement, leading to accidents and injury, and cause memory loss.
- It can lead to disturbed sleep or, conversely, passing out, which could result in serious injury.
- You may put on weight and experience dry skin.
- You will have an increased risk of cancer.
- Long-term drinking has been linked to anxiety, depression and dementia.
- You could experience raised blood pressure, resulting in heart disease or stroke.
- It could lead to liver disease and pancreatitis.
- You could experience fertility issues.
- You will have an increased risk of osteoporosis.

 # BROKEN PROMISES

Alcohol is quite adept at telling us what we want to hear. But the reality often falls short. Just as in a toxic relationship, we convince ourselves that things are not as bad as they seem, but if we're being truthful, it's actually pretty painful. Here are just three of the promises alcohol makes (and breaks):

1. **I'll help you relax** – It is true that alcohol has tranquilizing properties, but many people report post-drinking anxiety – a vague sense of agitation and unease as the alcohol leaves your body the following day. It may help calm you down for a few hours, but the overall effect of alcohol consumption is greater anxiety for a longer period.

2. **I'll help you get to sleep** – Alcohol can have a disastrous effect on sleep patterns, particularly in the second part of the night when we enter a lighter sleep phase. This is because it prevents us from achieving the restful sleep we need to feel energized for the following day. No wonder we can't be bothered to get out of our pyjamas on a Sunday morning.

3. **I'll make life more fun** – It's easy to get sucked in by this one. Alcohol appeals to many of us because it gives everything a rosy glow and a temporary feeling that all is well. In moderation this is true, but if you're starting to rely on alcohol as a crutch to make everything in life seem better, it might be time to reassess your consumption.

 # BAD CHEMISTRY

Drinking alcohol can interfere with the chemicals in our brain that are responsible for our thoughts, feelings and actions. It's a delicate balance, and happy thoughts can quite quickly tip over into negative emotions. This is because alcohol is a depressant. It temporarily suppresses emotions like anxiety and our inhibitions, but the more we drink, the more likely it is that the result will be a feeling of depression and low mood. In heavy drinkers, there is also a strong association between chronic alcohol misuse, self-harm and suicide. Drinking heavily can also lower the level of serotonin in our brain – that's the chemical responsible for balancing our moods – leaving us feeling anxious and unhappy. Put simply, the more we drink, the more likely it is that we'll be compromising our long-term mental health.

IT'LL MAKE YOU WANT TO COMFORT EAT

Unfortunately, the scales don't lie and when it comes to weight gain alcohol has a lot to answer for. Not only is alcohol packed full of empty calories – even wine, which with a calorie count of up to 200 per glass is equivalent to eating a Mars bar – but research shows that we actually *crave* food if we're drinking, because the neurons in our brain that tell us we're hungry are fired up by alcohol. And because our judgement is impaired and we're feeling a bit gung-ho about life, we're much more likely to bury our face in a bag of crisps and a pizza than spend time preparing a nice healthy salad. There's a good reason those jeans are getting tighter and it's got nothing to do with the temperature of the washing machine.

IT'LL BREAK YOUR HEART

Quite literally. Drinking regularly or drinking too much on a single occasion can put undue stress on your heart and cause irreversible damage. Problems can include:

- **Cardiomyopathy** – Where the heart muscles become overly stretched and droopy, thick or stiff, affecting the heart's ability to pump blood around the body.
- **Arrhythmia** – An irregular heartbeat, or a heartbeat that is too fast or slow. Complications of arrhythmia include stroke, cardiac arrest and heart failure.
- **High blood pressure** – Untreated, this can lead to heart disease, a heart attack or stroke.
- **Stroke** – This can potentially lead to paralysis or loss of muscle movement, memory loss and difficulty in talking or swallowing.

Numerous studies have revealed the close link between alcohol consumption and high blood pressure. If you consume more than three drinks in one sitting, the rise is temporary, but regular binge-drinking can result in long-term raised blood pressure.

If your heart must work harder to get blood around your body, it has a knock-on effect on your arteries, which can struggle to cope with the increase in pressure. This, coupled with artery hardening caused by an increase in lipids (fats) in the bloodstream after alcohol consumption, could potentially overwhelm an already struggling organ. We only get one heart and once it's broken it's not an easy fix.

IT'LL MAKE YOU SICK TO YOUR STOMACH

From indigestion to vomiting and stomach ulcers – it's safe to say our stomachs weren't designed to cope with the toxic effects of alcohol.

Alcohol can weaken the acidity of our stomach acid, which we need to break down food and absorb nutrients. This can lead to harmful bacteria entering our upper intestines, causing irritation and infection, as well as gastritis (inflammation of the stomach) and peptic ulcers.

Alcohol can also exacerbate acid reflux, which causes nausea and burning pain in the chest. This is because alcoholic drinks like beer and wine encourage our stomachs to produce more acid, as well as relaxing the lower oesophageal sphincter, which allows the contents of the stomach to leak back into the oesophagus. This, of course, is much more likely if you've enjoyed a skinful and then introduced your stomach to the delights of a 3 a.m. kebab.

IT INCREASES YOUR RISK OF CANCER

In the UK alone, it is thought that up to 12,800 cases of cancer annually could be avoided if we drank less. Alcohol can cause seven different types of cancer – mouth, upper throat, larynx, oesophagus, breast, liver and bowel – and harms us in three different ways:

- **Acetaldehyde** – Our bodies convert alcohol into this toxic-sounding chemical, which can then go on to wreak havoc with our DNA and prevent cells from repairing the damage.
- **Hormone changes** – We need hormones to give our cells vital instructions – such as knowing when to grow and divide, and when not to – but alcohol interferes with this process.
- **Increased absorption** – Alcohol can affect the cells in the throat and mouth, making it easier for other carcinogens to be absorbed.

This is true of ALL alcohol, regardless of strength, but cutting down reduces your risk.

FROM FIZZLE TO FLOP

We've all been there. From the disappointing drunken fumble that leaves you blushing the next day, to the full-on walk of shame the following morning – alcohol and sex often go hand in hand. Unfortunately, this often doesn't translate to *good* sex. For men, too much alcohol can make maintaining an erection an impossibility and long-term drinking can cause impotence. Women can look forward to vaginal dryness – making penetration uncomfortable – and difficulty in achieving an orgasm. Throw into the mix issues with balance and coordination, and reduced sensitivity, and it could go from fizzle to flop very quickly. At the more sinister end of the scale, alcohol impairs judgement and reduces our inhibitions. If you've had too much to drink you might take risks you wouldn't normally take, such as having unprotected sex or going home with a stranger.

THE SLEEP THIEF

Alcohol might make you fall asleep quicker, but the quality of your sleep is likely to be impaired. Why? Because it disrupts the REM (rapid eye movement) stage of sleep, which is an essential rest period for our brains. Incidentally, REM sleep is when we dream, which is an essential part of memory and emotional processing. If we don't get enough REM sleep, we feel drowsy, irritable and mentally sluggish the following day. Alcohol also relaxes the muscles in the head, neck and throat, causing snoring – which if it doesn't disrupt your sleep will almost certainly disrupt everyone else's. There's also a good chance you'll need to get up to go to the toilet, and since alcohol is a diuretic and encourages our bodies to lose extra fluid, you'll probably feel clammy, too – delightful.

GOODBYE FIT AND HEALTHY, HELLO GERMS AND VIRUSES

Alcohol has the potential to compromise our immune system, increasing our risk of catching illnesses and infections. When we're exposed to a virus, our bodies mount an immune response to attack and kill the foreign pathogen, but alcohol makes it harder for our immune system to get ready for the fight and defend our bodies against harmful germs. If you're a regular drinker, you'll probably notice you feel more run down and catch colds, coughs and the flu more often than your non-drinking friends. In our lungs, for example, alcohol damages the immune cells and fine hairs that clear pathogens out of the way. Alcohol can also trigger inflammation in the gut, and destroy the microorganisms that live in our intestines and help to kill harmful bacteria.

IT CAN COMPROMISE YOUR FERTILITY

Alcohol can reduce fertility in both men and women. Apart from the fact that doing the deed itself is often more challenging (for all the reasons already discussed), research shows that if a woman drinks between one and five alcoholic drinks a week it can reduce her chances of conceiving, and ten drinks or more reduce the chances even further. Regular drinking can also cause hormonal fluctuations, leading to irregular ovulation and periods, and in severe cases it can stop a woman's periods completely.

For men, excessive alcohol consumption lowers testosterone levels and sperm quality and quantity. It can also reduce a man's libido and in the long term cause impotence. The good news is that, if you reduce what you drink, these effects can be quickly reversed.

IT'S BAD NEWS FOR YOUR BRAIN

We all know alcohol can leave us feeling fuzzy-headed in the short term, but did you know that the effect alcohol has on our brain far outlasts a hangover? Consistent use of alcohol depletes neurotransmitters and alters our brain function.

A study published in the *British Medical Journal* found that just one glass a day caused concerning changes. The changes included three times the risk (compared with non-drinkers) of right-sided hippocampal atrophy – a type of brain damage that can impact spatial navigation and long-term memory, and potentially lead to Alzheimer's and dementia.

Even in small amounts, alcohol affects our cognitive ability, compromising our attention, judgement, memory, sleep and coordination. These functions are all made possible by the cerebrum – the topmost part of the brain, which is responsible for the ability to think.

Heavy drinking may have extensive effects on the brain, ranging from memory loss all the way through to debilitating conditions and brain damage that require round-the-clock medical care. In a study published in *Alcoholism: Clinical & Experimental Research*, researchers looked at how the amount of alcohol consumed affected people's day-to-day memory. It showed that a typically heavy drinker reported more than 30 per cent more memory-related problems than someone who reportedly did not drink, and almost 25 per cent more issues than a person who stated they drank only small amounts of alcohol.

Not all hope is lost, however. Research shows that a resurgence of new brain cells is possible within a year of cutting down or abstaining from alcohol. That's something to raise a mocktail for.

IT'LL SUCK THE LIFE OUT OF YOUR SKIN

Unless you relish looking like a prune, drinking alcohol is particularly unkind to our skin. When we drink, our bodies become dehydrated, and because skin is our largest bodily organ it's one of the first things to be affected. Skin is quick to lose its natural plumpness and glow if we don't keep hydrated, leading to duller skin, wrinkles and visible pores. Filling ourselves with the empty calories and sugars found in our favourite beverage is also bad news for our nutrition – and we need nutrients and vitamins to keep our skin in tip-top condition. Research has also shown that alcohol, specifically white wine and spirits, increases the risk of rosacea – a condition that causes long-term redness and facial swelling. Alcohol can also cause skin inflammation, leading to acne and spots. "Margarita Monday" suddenly just lost its appeal...

WHAT THE EYE DOESN'T SEE...

Just like our skin, eyes can quickly become dry and irritated if we're not hydrated enough. Aside from the obvious drawbacks of having itchy and inflamed eyes, alcohol also swells the small blood vessels, making them appear red and bloodshot. If we've really overdone it, there's a good chance our vision will become blurred and distorted, risking accidents and injuries. Alcohol also decreases the reaction times of our pupils, leading to light sensitivity and colour distortion. These may seem like minor issues, but research shows that long-term heavy drinking can permanently damage the optic nerve – which carries messages from the eye to the brain – leading to loss of vision in severe cases. It's not worth turning a blind eye – but bad pun aside, consuming less alcohol really is fundamental to protecting our eyesight.

WHEN BOOZE TURNS TO BALD

If you're a fan of a liquid lunch and more likely to hit the bottle than prepare yourself a healthy meal, then there's a good chance you're denying your body the vital nutrients and vitamins it needs to maintain healthy hair. Even if you eat well, alcohol has an annoying habit of interfering with the body's absorption of all the good bits in food because it irritates the stomach lining and can increase acid production. Dehydration damages hair follicles, meaning our previously luscious locks are likely to feel brittle and a bit bleurgh. If alcohol has sucked the life out of your scalp, it's likely you'll end up losing more than just flakes of dandruff, too. Time to invest in a hat.

IT TURNS EXERCISE INTO A CHORE

Whether you enjoy a gentle stroll or you're a member of the local football team, alcohol can affect your ability to exercise effectively. Alcohol is a diuretic, so it increases the amount of urine our kidneys produce, leaving us dehydrated. Exercise – if we're really going for it – makes us sweat, and the combined effects of sweating and the diuretic effect of alcohol make dehydration much more likely. Hydration during exercise is essential to maintaining normal blood flow to our organs, which plays a crucial role in ensuring oxygen and nutrients reach our muscles. Alcohol also interferes with our metabolism, causing low blood sugar, which in turn leads to decreased energy levels and performance. It can also compromise our motor skills, and slower reaction times and impaired hand–eye coordination could easily lead to a ball in the face. Ouch.

IT'S BAD FOR YOUR BONES

Research shows that chronic drinking, especially during our young adult years, can dramatically affect the health of our bones, leading to osteoporosis later in life. This is because alcohol and calcium are not on the best of terms – and we need calcium to keep our bones strong. When we drink, it makes it harder for our small intestine to absorb calcium. Alcohol also interferes with the pancreas and its ability to absorb vitamin D – and we need vitamin D to aid calcium absorption.

Some studies also suggest that alcohol decreases oestrogen levels in our bodies. As oestrogen levels decline our bones lose the ability to regenerate and bone deterioration can occur. The risk is increased if you're a woman of menopausal age because it can exacerbate the bone deterioration that naturally occurs during menopause.

And that's not all. Excessive alcohol consumption can also increase two potentially bone-destroying hormones: cortisol and parathyroid hormone. High levels of cortisol have been shown to decrease bone formation and increase bone breakdown, and chronic alcohol consumption can increase levels of parathyroid hormone, which leaches calcium from the bone. Heavy drinkers are particularly at risk of developing brittle bones, which makes them more likely to suffer fractures.

If you throw into the mix an increased likelihood of losing your balance when you've had too much to drink – and an overconfidence in your physical abilities – you could be looking at a trip to the hospital and a plaster cast.

 # IT CAN AFFECT OUR RELATIONSHIPS

Alcohol lowers our inhibitions and makes us feel more confident – fact. But once those inhibitions fall away, it can be difficult to exercise self-control, particularly in terms of what we do or say. Alcohol is often referred to as the "truth drug", and it is certainly true that alcohol's mood-changing abilities can lead us to say something we might later regret – also known as "foot in mouth" syndrome. This may result in a minor indiscretion that everyone can laugh about later, but it also has the potential to hurt those around us.

Also, because alcohol interferes with brain function, it can reduce our ability to act and think rationally, which can lead to an escalation in anger and aggressiveness – and even violence in the worst cases. One prominent medical theory – "alcohol myopia" – proposes that alcohol narrows our attention, meaning that we may miss the social and environmental cues that help us to interpret situations rationally. Misinterpreting the behaviour of others and being provoked when we've had too much to drink can also lead to a potentially explosive situation. While it is a challenging subject to confront, the evidence is clear. Police records in England and Wales in the years 2017/18 showed that victims of violent attacks believed their aggressor(s) to be under the influence of alcohol in 39 per cent of incidents.

It is tempting in minor situations to use alcohol as an excuse for bad behaviour, but if you frequently argue with those around you when you've consumed alcohol and it's beginning to negatively affect your relationships, it's probably time to consider making some long-term changes to your drinking habits.

IT DOESN'T LOVE YOUR LIVER

Most alcohol we consume is processed by the liver, and if we consistently work it too hard by over-drinking there's a chance its health will begin to suffer. The liver is already an overstretched organ – it has more than 500 different functions, including processing the nutrients absorbed from digested food and combating infection – so it doesn't really need the extra strain of an afternoon in the pub. If the liver has to break down too much alcohol, particularly over a sustained period, its other functions are negatively affected. In the long term, drinking can cause fatty liver, hepatitis (inflammation of the liver) and cirrhosis (scarring of the liver), and in the worst cases liver cancer. In the UK, around 7,700 people die each year due to alcohol-related liver disease and, although it's preventable, these numbers continue to increase.

COUNTING THE COST

As if all the negative health effects of alcohol weren't bad enough, it also burns a hole in our pockets. The Office for National Statistics reports that from April 2019 to March 2020 the average UK household spent £473 on alcohol to drink at home. In the US, this figure was $579 for the year 2019, according to the Bureau of Labor Statistics. When it comes to nights out, we often forget about the hidden costs – the taxis home, the takeaways and fast food – not to mention the fact that alcohol affects our judgement, meaning we're more likely to have "just one more", even though we probably shouldn't. Alcohol also makes us more prone to losing and breaking things – and, as anyone who has had to replace a smartphone after a night out will confirm, it's a painful (and sobering) experience.

WHERE TO START

Improved mood. Better sleep. More energy. More money. Sound good? Cutting back the amount of alcohol we consume can have a positive effect within a matter of days. In the long term it can dramatically reduce our risk of serious health conditions. We know what we want the outcome to be, but where do we start? It's important to know that reducing our alcohol intake doesn't have to be an entire life change unless we want it to be. Arming ourselves with strategies, knowing and understanding our triggers, staying within the low-risk drinking guidelines and ensuring we have "drink-free" days every week might seem like small steps, but altogether they can have a big impact.

PLANNING FOR CHANGE

One of the reasons we find ourselves agreeing to have a drink is because we haven't had a clear intention in our minds to say no.

Before you start to make changes, invest in some thinking time – remind yourself why you want to cut back and what you hope to achieve. Think about which situations might be hard to navigate – such as meeting up with friends or family – and consider how to approach them from now on. Decide ahead of time how to refuse "just one more" – pre-prepared phrases come in useful here, such as "I've decided to make a positive change" or "I've made a commitment to myself to get healthier". Remember – you don't owe anyone an explanation, but even if you don't voice these reasons out loud, you can use them as a motivational mantra.

TELL YOUR TRIBE

Putting the people you love in the picture will help to make sure there are no awkward moments when you refuse a drink. If they know your intentions, then they'll know not to put temptation within arm's reach! Friends and family are also quite useful for giving pep-talks when your enthusiasm starts to wane, as well as being your biggest cheerleaders when things are going well. The more people you tell, the more accountability you'll have – meaning you're more likely to stick it out.

 # KEEP A DRINK DIARY

Keep a drink diary for a few weeks. This will help you decide what levels of drinking you're comfortable with and what you're not. It will also help you see if any patterns emerge – for instance, do you regularly overdo it on a weekend? Or are there people who you always end up drinking more with than you'd ideally like to? Sometimes seeing the facts in black and white makes them harder to ignore – which is a good thing! Remember to note how many units you drink; you'll probably be surprised how quickly they add up.

There are also many apps that are designed exactly for this purpose. They often include goal-setting, unit calculators, motivational tips and advice – plus you can carry them around in your pocket, so no excuses!

DISCOVER YOUR TRIGGERS

Often, we subconsciously build an association between alcohol and certain times of day or specific situations. Before we know it, it's become an automatic response and we're not even aware we've reached for the bottle until we're staring at an empty glass. Being more mindful of our triggers can help us to break the association and form a new, healthier one. So, what are your triggers?

Drinking with dinner – Dinner and drinks go hand in hand for many of us, but one drink can easily turn into several. Try water alongside alcohol to help space out your drinking.

Drinking after work – After a long day at work, it's tempting to reach for a bottle of wine to help you relax. Have a think about what else you can do to unwind in the evening – what about a new hobby? Or some light exercise?

Getting the kids to bed – Always worthy of celebration, this one is especially hard to break, particularly if you've spent an hour wrestling with a recalcitrant toddler. Have a treat planned that you can indulge in once you've succeeded – run a bubble bath or snuggle up under a blanket and watch a film.

Your partner wants to drink – The bottle's already open, but you've resolved to have a drink-free evening. Can you resist? If you've got the willpower to say, "No, thanks", kudos to you; but if you know you're going to find it hard, why not compromise instead? Make a pact to only have a glass each with dinner, or – even better – leave the alcohol to them and try a non-alcoholic option instead.

KNOW YOUR UNITS

We know we're not supposed to drink "too much", but how much is too much? And how many of us know what a unit of alcohol is? With so many different options and sizes of measure it can be easy to get confused.

Current UK low-risk drinking guidelines recommend it's safest for both men and women to limit their intake to no more than 14 units a week. The current recommendation in the US is no more than one alcoholic drink a day for women and two for men. Wherever you are in the world, keeping a note of how much alcohol you're consuming in a week can be a useful tool for working out whether you could benefit from cutting back.* In the UK, the following applies:

* It's important to recognize that guidelines differ depending on where you are in the world – always check with your healthcare provider to make sure you're following the correct guidance.

TYPE OF DRINK	NUMBER OF ALCOHOLIC UNITS
Single small shot of spirits – gin, vodka, whisky, rum, tequila, sambuca (25 ml)	1 unit
Single large measure of spirits (35 ml)	1.4 units
Alcopop (275 ml)	1.5 units
Small glass of red/white/ rosé wine (125 ml)	1.5 units
Bottle of lager/beer/cider (330 ml)	1.6 units
Large can of lager/beer/cider (440 ml)	2 units
Pint of lower-strength (< 3.6% ABV) lager/beer/cider	2 units
Standard glass of red/white/rosé wine (175 ml)	2.1 units
Pint of higher-strength (> 5.2% ABV) lager/beer/cider	3 units
Large glass of red/white/ rosé wine (250 ml)	3 units

Knowing how much alcohol you're consuming helps you stay in control. Aim to spread units over at least three days, but ideally over the course of the week, with drink-free days in between.

BE MINDFUL OF HOME MEASURES

Unless you've earned your stripes working behind a bar or happen to have a set of drinks measures at home, there's a fair chance that every time you pour a drink you're relying on guesswork to obtain the right quantity. Clue – the measures are smaller than you think.

If we remove the element of "guesstimation", we have a much better chance of moderating our alcohol intake and avoiding accidentally overindulging. The good news is drinks measures aren't just for your local pub – you can purchase a set yourself, which will help you be more accurate and make it easier to track how much you're drinking. You're welcome.

INVENT YOUR OWN MOCKTAIL

It's time to tap into your inner mixologist. Low or alcohol-free options used to be few and far between and tasteless, but they've improved so much in recent years that they're winning awards over their full-strength competitors. Let's all raise a glass to that.

Most supermarkets now have alcohol-free options, including alcohol-free spirits, which means we can make our own mocktails at home. Turn this into a fun activity and get creative. And if you're lacking inspiration, you can always check out the mocktail recipes included in this book. Start by replacing one alcoholic drink a week with a mocktail or other alcohol-free option, and gradually introduce more over time. Happy mixing!

CORK IT, STORE IT, FREEZE IT

You've opened a bottle of wine and had a glass or two, but there's still some left. It would be a waste not to drink it now, wouldn't it?

The average bottle of wine can contain 10 units of alcohol, which means if you regularly consume a bottle in one go, you'll be risking long-term health problems.

It's a common misconception that wine doesn't "keep". If you use an airtight cork, it should last a couple of days at least. You can also freeze it in an ice-cube tray and use it to add extra flavour when you cook. White wine is great with fish – add it to a white sauce and eat with your favourite seafood, or splash some into a paella or risotto. Red wine works brilliantly with meat dishes such as stews, in gravies and in Bolognese sauces.

SURVIVING THE BIG NIGHT OUT

A ban on booze doesn't have to be boring. There's no reason why you can't still enjoy a night out with friends – you just need to switch up your thinking. Next time you're planning to go out drinking, try the following to help you limit your alcohol intake but still have fun:

- **Set a limit before you go out and stick to it.** Share your plan with a friend for added accountability.
- **Alternate alcoholic drinks with soft drinks.** It'll help you stay hydrated, too.
- **Eat a sensible meal before you go out.** It will help counter the effects of any alcohol you do drink and stop you shovelling pizza into your mouth at midnight.
- **Avoid rounds at all costs.** Once someone suggests rounds, everyone ends up drinking at pace, meaning you'll end up not only drinking more but spending more, too.

HAVE DRINK-FREE DAYS

Abstaining from drinking for a day gives our bodies a chance to rest, which is good for our immune system and mental health. Over time, you may even find that you're having more drink-free days than drinking days during the week, which is great! You could even try an extended period, such as two weeks or a month. Dry January is always a popular time to give this a go, as many of us tend to overindulge over the festive season, and you'll be able to gain momentum knowing you're part of a much bigger movement. On drink-free days, aim to fill your time with a different activity. For example, you could:

- Go for a walk or run.
- Try mastering a new dish in the kitchen.
- Bake something delicious.
- Follow a yoga video.
- Keep your hands busy with knitting or crochet.
- Start learning a new language.

CLEAR THE COUNTER

It may sound simple but making sure the paraphernalia we associate with drinking – bottles, wine glasses, corkscrews, etc. – are cleared away can really help keep us on track. Often, our environment can be a trigger for habitual behaviour – we see it, we want it. After all, if it's out of sight, it'll be out of mind, too.

TREAT YOURSELF

Got your eye on a new coat? Or perhaps you're lusting after a new gadget or something for your house? When you set yourself a drink-less goal, make sure you attach a reward to it, too. Knowing you're working towards something, in addition to all the recognized health benefits of cutting down, will help to keep you motivated and on track. The good news is, if you're drinking less, you'll be spending less. Set aside the cash you would have spent on alcohol and use it for your treat instead!

SWITCH UP THE VENUE

You can meet your friends and family in places other than a pub or bar. Wait, what?

There are so many alternative and equally buzzy venues where you can hang out with your favourite people – think coffee shops, cafés, restaurants and even juice bars – and have just as much fun. If you're not in the presence of alcohol, there will be no temptation to have a drink "just because it's there". In the summer, instead of lolling around a beer garden, why not make a picnic and head for the park or countryside? You'll be getting bonus exercise points if you include a walk, making it an infinitely healthier alternative. Changing meet-up times can help, too – you're less likely to drink while having breakfast or brunch than you are at the end of the day.

KNOW YOUR "NO"

It's easy to underestimate the importance of saying the right sort of "no". If you know drinks are on the cards, but you want to give it a miss, you need to be ready with a convincing, "No, thanks." It's worth investing some thinking time in this one and having a resistance strategy lined up in advance. The goal is to make it firm yet friendly, and avoid getting into a long discussion about the why, what and when of your decision – the more the conversation is dragged out, the more likely it is you'll get talked around and give in. Remember the following:

- Don't hesitate, as it'll give you a chance to talk yourself out of it – or the person offering a drink the chance to talk you around.
- Make and maintain eye contact.
- Keep your response short and to the point.

It's also a good idea to have some "end of discussion" responses up your sleeve in case you have an overly persistent friend who is intent on spoiling your hard work. These friends are usually identifiable by their constant refrain of, "Oh, go on, you know you want to" – in which case, it's time to get assertive. Try the following sequence of responses if they get stuck on repeat:

- After they ask you the first time – "No, thank you."
- After they ask the second time – "Not today, I don't want to."
- After they ask for a third time – "I'm giving alcohol a miss now because I want to be healthier/I'm making a positive change/I want to feel better about myself. It would be great if you could help me out and support my decision."

MINDFULNESS AND MEDITATION

Mindfulness is great for our well-being and it really comes into its own as a strategy to help combat alcohol cravings. Research has shown that 11 minutes a day can help heavy drinkers to cut back on their alcohol consumption. The study, carried out by University College London, found participants were drinking on average 9.3 fewer units (around three large glasses of wine) the week after they practised mindfulness.

Mindfulness encourages us to focus on the present and reconnect with ourselves – specifically our emotions, thoughts and bodily sensations. The theory goes that if we're more awake to ourselves, we'll be better able to control our cravings. If we practise every day, we can gradually train ourselves to notice when our thoughts and cravings are taking over, and understand that these are just mental events that do not have to control us. Mindfulness is also great for stress and anxiety. Meditation exercises can be a useful tool for controlling our alcohol consumption. Try the following:

- Set a timer for 10 minutes and sit cross-legged on a cushion.
- Rest your hands in your lap with your palms facing upwards.
- Keep your head still and your spine erect – it'll help you sit still for longer.
- Close your eyes and take deep breaths. Slowly let your breathing return to its natural rhythm. Be aware of every inhalation and exhalation. Be conscious of the rise and fall of your chest. Don't control the process; just let it happen.
- If your mind starts to wander, bring it back to your breath.
- Aim to sit as still as possible so that your mind isn't distracted by other sensations.

BUY SMALLER GLASSES

If you love wine and you know your Châteauneuf-du-Pape from your Brachetto d'Acqui, buying small (125 ml) wine glasses will help you resist the temptation to quaff half a bottle in one sitting. Large (250 ml) glasses encourage us to drink more, so just pour one small glass and then put the bottle away. Every time we choose a large glass over a small glass, we're consuming double the number of alcoholic units, which means it's easier for us to consume over the recommended 14 units a week without even noticing. A study published in *The Lancet* found that the risks for a 40-year-old of drinking over the recommended daily limit were comparable to the risks associated with smoking. It also found that every glass over the daily recommended limit will cut half an hour from the expected lifespan of a 40-year-old.

MAKE MIXERS THE MAIN EVENT

If you can't bear to part with your large wine glasses, you can always cheat! Spritzers make a refreshing and low-alcohol alternative to a whole glass of wine – meaning you can sip away guilt-free. You'll also be cheating your brain into thinking you're having a large glass when you're only drinking a small one. It'll help you pace yourself, too, as it'll take longer to finish. Lemonade or soda water are always popular choices with white wine or rosé, and you could always try cola with red wine. Called *calimocho*, this retro Spanish drink dates from the 1970s and has become a popular lower-alcohol alternative in recent years. Add mint leaves and sliced lemon for added flavour, and serve over ice for maximum refreshment.

CHECK IN WITH YOUR PROGRESS

Each week make sure you revisit your goal and revise it if necessary. You might find you're absolutely smashing it, in which case – hurrah! – you can up the ante and set yourself a more challenging goal, such as going for a longer stretch alcohol-free. If you've had a slip-up or you haven't quite achieved what you wanted to, don't beat yourself up. If you didn't hit your goal this week, reset your expectations and plan to make a fresh start next week.

 # AVOID SALTY FOOD

It may sound obvious, but salty food makes us thirsty and therefore more likely to drink at pace. If you're in a pub or bar, try to avoid peanuts and crisps. If the temptation gets too much, order a glass of water to go with them so you can quench your thirst the healthy way and pace your alcohol consumption. Make sure you eat before you go out to help combat those snack cravings. Likewise, if you're drinking at home, try not to make a beeline for the snack cupboard. If you are at home, the good news is you've probably got more food choices – make the most of that by choosing something low in salt. Unsalted popcorn, breadsticks and crackers all make good low-sodium alternatives.

 # FIND A TEAMMATE

Encouraging a friend or family member to join you on your drink-less journey is helpful for sharing advice as well as providing mutual support.

If your partner wants to cut back – brilliant! If you're both on the same page, it's a goal you can tackle together. Research shows that making a joint plan to cut back has the potential to be more successful than trying to make changes alone. Work together towards a shared vision of what your relationship could be like with less alcohol – you'll have more energy for doing the things you both enjoy and more headspace for each other. You'll be saving double the money, too. Spend some time together considering what you'll do with it instead. The key is to encourage and support each other – it'll bring you closer together and foster a sense of joint achievement.

 # RESET THE CLOCK

If you find yourself beginning to drink at a certain time every day – for instance when you finish work – try pushing the time you start drinking back a bit. You'll have fewer hours ahead of you before the end of the day in which to indulge, meaning you'll end up drinking less. Keep yourself busy; otherwise you'll spend an agonizing hour or two clock-watching – you could video-call a friend, go for a walk or distract yourself with a hobby. Gradually push the time back a bit further every day for maximum results.

A word of caution: if you're an evening drinker it's probably not a good idea to have your long-awaited drink just before bed, as it will result in bad sleep and night-time toilet trips.

SET A BUDGET

Set yourself an alcohol budget – either weekly or monthly – which you can adjust downwards as you progress towards your goal. Put any extra money you save to one side – for treats, naturally. A good way of ensuring you stick to your budget is to take the money out in cash at the beginning of the week or month. Having a visual reminder of what you've already spent is a good motivator to spend less.

If you're planning a night out, take your spending money out of your budget and leave your debit/credit card at home. You'll be less tempted (and less able) to spend more than you intended. Make up some forfeits to self-impose should you overspend your budget, such as tackling neglected household chores. The thought of an afternoon clearing gutters should be all the motivation you need!

 # TOUGH IT OUT

There will inevitably be times when you start to question whether it's worth it. Even cutting back on semi-regular drinking can sometimes cause challenging withdrawal symptoms: irritability, brain fog and poor concentration, feeling a bit shaky and clammy, to name just a few. The most important thing is to hang on in there and ride it out. If you keep going, it will pass. Better days and better health are on the horizon – and that's the only reason you need to stick it out. If you're really struggling, it might be time to seek professional support. Share your concerns with your doctor or primary care provider to make sure you're getting the right help.

CUTTING OUT ALCOHOL

Giving up alcohol can have an even bigger impact on your health and well-being than just cutting down. An astonishing 6.5 million people in the UK took part in Dry January in 2021. Of those, 70 per cent of people said they slept better, 86 per cent saved money and 65 per cent saw an overall improvement to their health.

And that's after only a month. Imagine the gains if you stopped drinking in the long term. So, what's stopping you? Read on to find out how to wave goodbye to alcohol for good.

 LET'S GET PREPARED

Before you begin your going-sober journey it's a good idea to check whether you're experiencing any of the signs and symptoms of alcohol dependence. Those who are dependent on alcohol are more likely to suffer from severe alcohol withdrawal, which can be dangerous without appropriate support from a medical professional. If you're experiencing any of the following symptoms, speak to your doctor or an alcohol support service to get advice on the safest way for you to quit drinking:

- Planning your day and social events around alcohol.
- Drinking compulsively and not being able to stop once you start.
- Feeling like you need an alcoholic drink to get going in the morning.

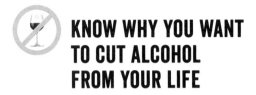

KNOW WHY YOU WANT TO CUT ALCOHOL FROM YOUR LIFE

If your relationship with alcohol has gone sour, it's probably time to pull the plug on it completely – but it's important you have a clear reason in mind, personal to you, as to why you want to break off your relationship with alcohol. By making it personal, you've got a much better chance of seeing it through. When the going gets tough – and it will – reminding yourself "why" will give you the motivation to walk away from alcohol for good.

ONE DAY AT A TIME

Focusing on one drink-free day at a time helps to keep expectations realistic and makes the overall journey seem more manageable. There are no shortcuts to giving up alcohol and those who've achieved it often compare the journey to a marathon rather than a sprint. When things get tough, remind yourself how amazing you'll feel when alcohol no longer controls your life.

In the early days, put yourself in the right frame of mind when you wake up in the morning by saying to yourself, "Today will be a drink-free day." By making an affirmation in this way, you'll be more accountable for your actions – and more likely to stick to it.

BREAKING BAD (HABITS)

Alcohol is a habit for many of us, but if we want to cut it from our lives, we need to make sure we're framing it in the right terms. Habits can be good (eating five portions of fruit and vegetables a day) or bad (smoking and drinking), and knowing whether we want to form a new good habit or break an old bad one can make it easier for us to achieve our goals.

Habits are formed in the following way:

- **Cue** – "Hurrah, I've finished work!"
- **Craving** – "What can I do to relax?"
- **Response** – "I know, I'll open that bottle of wine I bought earlier."
- **Reward** – "I've got that warm, fuzzy feeling and I can feel my worries slipping away."

But just because a habit can satisfy our cravings, it doesn't make it good.

The trick is to not allow alcohol onto your daily agenda. Think about ways you can make that harder

– this is the key to breaking the habit. For instance, drive a different route home from work so that you don't go past certain shops; don't have alcohol in the house so that the temptation isn't there in the first place; or remind yourself how alcohol leaves you feeling more bleurgh than blessed.

Try finding a different habit to replace the one you're trying to break – it needs to be easy to maintain, preferably something you enjoy, and it needs to give you the same reward but in a healthier way. Exercise is a fantastic substitute because it releases endorphins – the body's feel-good chemicals – and has the added benefit of being good for our overall health and mental well-being.

MINDSET MANTRAS

Mantras are calming, almost meditative phrases that we can repeat to ourselves to help us achieve a desired outcome. They are personal to our circumstances and can be adapted depending on whether we need them to be motivational, soothing or supportive of a decision or belief.

When alcohol starts to intrude on your thoughts, try repeating a mantra to distract yourself and stay on track, such as:

- **"Take it one day at a time"** – Looking too far into the future can be overwhelming. Keep things in perspective and just focus on the day ahead.

- **"You can do this"** – This is a great one to pick yourself up if you're starting to flag. Believe it and you'll make it a reality.

- **"I am in control, alcohol is not"** – Reassert your power and be strong in the face of temptation. You've got this.

- **"I will not drink alcohol today, no matter what"** – If a situation occurs in which your default is to reach for a bottle, such as getting home after a stressful day at work, repeat this mantra until you've calmed your thoughts.

- **"I am on a journey and I'm heading in the right direction"** – Every day without alcohol is a victory for your mind and body. Embrace the fact that with every day you're moving further away from the negative effects of alcohol and closer to a positive future.

 # CONNECT WITH A TEETOTAL TRIBE

Surround yourself with a sober squad who understand the journey to teetotal town. They'll be able to provide you with advice, tips and, most importantly, support if you hit a bump in the road. And, likewise, you can provide the same. Making it a team effort is helpful for sustaining motivation towards a shared goal. It also means you can celebrate milestones and anniversaries together – with mocktails, of course!

Speak to your doctor or healthcare provider – they'll be able to signpost you towards local face-to-face support groups of like-minded souls. Alternatively, you could join an online community. Here are a few ideas:

- **Club Soda** – A UK-based free online community. The website also has a blog that includes going-sober advice and ideas for alcohol-free alternatives.

- **Living Sober** – Based in New Zealand, this online community encourages participants to talk openly about their relationship with alcohol in a safe, friendly environment.

- **Hello Sunday Morning** – An Australian subscription-based online community that also includes a handy support app to assist you on your alcohol-free journey.

- **This Naked Mind** – A US-based website that offers advice and real-life inspirational stories about going sober, as well as a free resource section to get you started on your journey.

DO YOUR RESEARCH

There are some fantastic books available for those looking to make the change to an alcohol-free lifestyle. While many are written by healthcare professionals and experts who really know their stuff, the most inspirational are often written by recovering alcoholics or those who've battled their drink demons and made it out the other side.

Look for a resource that offers a balance between practical advice that will help you break the habit and relatable experiences to keep you engaged in the process. Some helpful titles include:

- *The Unexpected Joy of Being Sober* (2017) – Catherine Gray
- *Glorious Rock Bottom* (2020) – Bryony Gordon
- *Alcohol Explained: Understand Why You Drink and How to Stop* (2015) – William Porter

Many of them are also available as audio books, so you can listen while you're going about your day.

 # BOSSING IT

Who's the boss in this relationship? Alcohol or you? Sometimes it's easier to let alcohol dictate the terms. Remember how good it is at luring you in and telling you what you want to hear? But being a passive bystander will get you nowhere if you're trying to tell alcohol to go away for good. Alcohol may well occupy our thoughts when we're trying to quit, but it doesn't control our bodies – only you can tell your hand to reach for that glass and take a sip. Aim to quash any attempts alcohol makes to persuade you otherwise – drown it out with a mantra. Or remind yourself of how far you've come and that you deserve to be happy without alcohol. "Alcohol made me do it..." just won't cut it any more!

BE KIND TO YOURSELF

Now more than ever is the time to go easy on yourself. Giving up alcohol is a big deal and can leave you feeling more than a little vulnerable and exposed.

While you're on your drink-free journey, it's a good idea to avoid (where possible) stressful situations or decisions, such as moving to a new house, changing your job or taking exams – they may trigger your default setting and before you know it you'll be self-medicating with a glass of wine again. Instead, focus on self-care – spend some time discovering what really makes you happy and helps you let off steam. If you want to spend an hour in a bubble bath, just do it! Want to revisit a childhood hobby that you've neglected? What are you waiting for? Carve out some time for yourself and reconnect with your happy place.

 **STAY BUSY**

If you're just sitting around waiting for the days to pass you by and for your journey to sobertown to be complete, it's going to feel like even more of an uphill struggle than it already is. All that time brooding is also a recipe for intrusive thoughts, such as, "I can't do this" or "I want to stop trying", or worse – "I really need a drink". Don't give the drink demon a chance – get up, give yourself a shake and find something, *anything*, to do. You could:

- Do some long-neglected chores.
- Bake something for a friend.
- Go on a long walk or bike ride.
- Volunteer for a local charity.
- Learn to play a musical instrument.

START A DRINK-FREE JOURNEY JOURNAL

Writing things down can help us process our thoughts and emotions. Getting things out of our heads and onto the page – particularly negative thoughts – can be cathartic and helps keep things in perspective. Often problems appear less overwhelming when we reduce them down to words on a page. Keeping a journal is also helpful for recording progress – and it'll give you an amazing sense of achievement when you look back at the end of your journey. Use the following for inspiration to help get you started:

- Jot down how you're feeling today.
- Think about what you're hoping to achieve.
- Write a list of triggers you've identified and your plan for avoiding them.
- Brainstorm your motivations for going teetotal.
- Reflect on your ongoing progress and what you've achieved so far.

 # NAIL YOUR DIET

Making adjustments to our diet can help with withdrawal symptoms and assist us on our journey to soberville.

- **Reduce your salt intake.** Alcohol damages the liver and salt makes the situation worse by encouraging water retention, forcing the liver to work harder. Avoid processed food and salty snacks – grab some fruit and veg instead.

- **A drop in blood-sugar levels can trigger alcohol cravings, so keep them topped up.** Rather than reach for a quick fix like chocolate, choose carbohydrates with a low glycaemic index such as wholemeal pasta, nuts and cereals.

- **Proteins help to promote the absorption of key nutrients and cell regeneration, so ensure you're eating the right proteins every day** – such as lean chicken, fish, chickpeas and lentils – and cook them from fresh rather than relying on processed meat or ready meals.

 # GET MOVING

Exercise is the perfect replacement for alcohol. Not only does it give us a similar buzz to the one we get from alcohol – courtesy of the chemical dopamine, which is released when we have a drink and when we work out – but also we'll be getting physically fitter. Win-win.

Research suggests that using medical intervention alone to combat alcohol misuse has a relapse rate of 60–90 per cent within one year, but when physical exercise is introduced as a complementary treatment, participants are much more likely to quit for longer periods and often for good.

It can also help our bodies to heal. Sustained alcohol consumption can affect most of our major organs, including our kidneys, liver and heart – not to mention other parts of our bodies such as our skin and hair. Exercise strengthens our bodies on the inside as well as the outside, helping our organs return to a healthier state. It also supports brain function and helps to lift that pesky booze-induced "brain fog" and poor concentration.

Whether you're pounding the pavements on a run, walking around your nearest green space or rowing down the local river, exercise is brilliant for boosting your mood. Drinking too much can lead to depression, anxiety and poor self-image, leading to a negative mindset. However, the release of endorphins that exercise promotes helps to reduce stress and anxiety, as well as combating negative thoughts. By committing to regular exercise, we're reminding ourselves that we're capable of working hard towards a goal and sticking to something, which boosts self-esteem.

Don't sit around fighting the temptation to drink – get up, get out and get moving!

DO IT FOR CHARITY

If you're no longer spending your pennies on alcohol, that's a lot of spare cash to play with. You *could* spend it on yourself – after all, it's a tempting amount. But have you considered donating that money to charity? Knowing that your hard work is benefiting others is a brilliant motivator, particularly when the going gets tough. You could put the money you've saved in a glass jar where you can see it so it's a visual reminder of your generosity, which will give you a sense of well-being, too. Choose a charity that has personal meaning to you for added inspiration.

MAKE THE MOST OF HANGOVER-FREE MORNINGS

Celebrate the joy of feeling good and not waking up with a tongue like sandpaper or heavy-metal-style drumming in your head. Cutting out alcohol means you no longer have to spend the morning-after-the-night-before recovering on the sofa and lamenting your life choices. You've gained time – make the most of it! Go outside, breathe in the fresh air and congratulate yourself on having a clear head and clarity of thought. Throw yourself back into a hobby that you've let lapse, or simply spend quality time with friends and family. Reconnect with things that make you feel alive – you've earned it.

LEARN TO LIKE YOURSELF SOBER

For many people, particularly those who misuse alcohol, drink begins to define who they think they are. For some, it's the perceived feeling of self-confidence and lack of inhibition that they enjoy. Many people are drawn to the sense of hedonistic excitement that an evening of drinking promises. Unfortunately, alcohol has a cunning way of making us believe that our personality is somehow better if we've had a drink, and that going sober will turn us into a boring loner – or worse, make us appear a "do-gooder". To make matters worse, all the events we consider "fun" often have an element of drinking attached to them – weddings, watching a show or a sporting event, family barbecues, pizza night... you name it, the alcohol's there lurking.

True, not having alcohol in your life will change you – but not in the ways you think. It's time we stopped seeing alcohol as a magic tonic that boosts every occasion and makes us and everything around us fabulous. You are fabulous on your own.

Embrace the fact that you know your own mind, have taken control of your destiny and are capable of being the best version of yourself without the crutch of alcohol. Feel every emotion without your senses being blunted by drink. Most importantly, know that you are fulfilling your potential each and every day, whether that's at work, with your family and friends, or on your own at home. Make each sober day count.

Teetotalism can be intoxicating too – you just need to give it a chance to work its own magic.

KEEPING IT UP

You've come this far and you're starting to see the benefits – better sleep, better health, better concentration... and you might have even lost some weight. It's taken grit and determination, so to make it all worthwhile you'll want to do everything you can to stay on track, right? Often the hardest part of the journey is sustaining the same momentum throughout and sometimes willpower alone just doesn't cut it. For the lucky few, staying sober and consciously choosing not to drink is so normal it isn't even a thing. And that's great! But most of us need a little more help. Luckily, there are plenty of things we can do to stop ourselves falling for alcohol's "charms" again.

IT'S OK IF YOU SLIP UP

First things first – it's OK if you slip up every now and again, as long as you learn from the experience. Getting sober is a sprint, but staying sober is a marathon with no finishing line. Having a glass of wine twice a year on special occasions isn't going to set you back, but when twice a year suddenly becomes twice a month and then twice a week, you'll be back to square one with only an aching head and self-loathing to keep you company. The trick is to always, *always* stay in control of your drinking. Don't give alcohol the chance to worm its way back in. You're in charge and you call the shots – just not the alcoholic kind…

LEARN TO RECOGNIZE THE WARNING SIGNS

Research shows around a third of people who are sober for less than a year will stay sober, but after a year, the rate increases to just under half. To give yourself the best chance of success, you need to recognize when you might be falling back into old habits. These can sneak up on us, so watch out for the following:

- Thinking about drinking throughout the day.
- Talking to other people about missing alcohol.
- Socializing with friends who are likely to encourage you to break your sobriety.
- Becoming isolated and withdrawn from friends and family.
- Experiencing increased anxiety or feeling depressed.
- Behaving secretively or lying to people around you.

BIGGING UP THE BENEFITS

Keeping the benefits of an alcohol-free life in mind can help to sustain us through the sticky spots. If you can stay on track, you've got a whole lot of fabulousness coming your way, including the following:

- Better-quality sleep.
- No hangovers and fewer headaches.
- A fuzz-free head and clarity of thought.
- Healthier hair, nails and skin.
- Stronger bones.
- Better digestion and a healthier gut.
- Weight loss.
- More money.
- Emotional stability.
- Improved sex life.
- Healthier relationships with those around you.
- More energy for doing the things you enjoy.
- Safeguarding your future health.
- An enhanced feeling of well-being knowing you're doing something positive.

CREATE A WATERTIGHT SCHEDULE

Become an absolute pro at time management. Devise a daily schedule or routine – write it down if you need to and put it somewhere obvious – and try your hardest to stick to it. Keeping busy will distract you from those annoying cravings or clock-watching, and it'll help to keep your mind off alcohol. There are a lot of hours in the day, so make sure you're making the most of each and every one of them. Having a routine helps to keep people grounded, and for many of us removing unpredictability and uncertainty helps us feel in control. It's also great for establishing healthier habits and helps to keep our focus on the important things – like not drinking.

CELEBRATE MILESTONES

Whether you're 30 days into your sober journey or you've clocked up 100 days and counting, make sure you're celebrating when you hit those milestones. Shout about it to anyone who'll listen, and share your news with friends and family. You've earned the right to be smug, so make the most of it. Staying alcohol-free isn't a punishment, it's a reward – so celebrate it.

BE THANKFUL

Studies have shown that reflecting on daily events that make us thankful can encourage us to use patience and restraint when dealing with stressful situations. When you feel the urge to pour yourself a drink, stop and remind yourself of everything you're thankful for – whether that's having a loving family or a roof over your head. Thinking about the things we're grateful for in life encourages a sense of well-being and helps to turn our thoughts away from negative situations. It also promotes a sense of optimism, which means we're more likely to stay on our journey to abstinence and hit our alcohol-free goals.

LET IT WASH OVER YOU

Whenever you feel the urge to run to the nearest bar, take a moment to stop and reflect on how that feels. Don't try to fight against the feeling. Instead, let it wash over you like a wave, knowing that once the wave has crashed and broken it will draw back, taking the desire to drink with it. Visualizing the craving in this way can help us to retain perspective and it provides a useful mental distraction when things get tough.

TRY SOMETHING NEW

Always wanted to learn how to roller-skate? Or perhaps you fancy dabbling in watercolour painting? Now is the time to introduce something new and different into your life. Mix things up and go out of your comfort zone. Aim to fill your time with something positive. Engaging in a new hobby gives us a new focus and a new set of goals, which helps to prevent the triggers that encourage us to drink – such as boredom, loneliness and negative thought patterns. If hobbies aren't your thing, what about volunteering? Most charity organizations are crying out for extra help, so why not put your new-found free time to good use? Knowing you're making a difference will give you a much better sense of well-being than a drink will ever be able to – and it'll cost you nothing.

KEEP REMINDING YOURSELF OF THE REASON WHY

YOU are your biggest champion and supporter and therefore it's YOU who you should turn to first when things get tough. Think about your original motivation for giving up alcohol. You might want to get healthier and make some positive changes in your life. Or perhaps you don't like the way alcohol makes you behave towards the people you care about. Whatever your reasons, keep reminding yourself why you're on your journey and it'll help you stay on track.

The opposite is also true. Asking ourselves why we feel the need to drink can also be helpful because it gives us a chance to analyze our behaviour and question our motivations. Chances are, the reasons to drink won't compare favourably with the reasons to be sober – so it's a bit of a no-brainer. *Au revoir*, alcohol!

THE IMPORTANCE OF VITAMINS

Going sober means our bodies are healing from the inside out. One of the reasons alcohol makes us feel so bad is because it inhibits our absorption of the vitamins and minerals we need to stay healthy. Make sure you're getting enough of the following:

- **Vitamin B complex** helps us to convert food into energy, acts as an antioxidant and assists our production of red blood cells. Good sources include wholegrain cereals, green vegetables such as broccoli and spinach, meat, fish, nuts, seeds, pulses, milk and eggs.
- **Omega-3** is found in oily fish such as mackerel or sardines. It helps to regulate our blood pressure, and prevents heart disease and high cholesterol.
- **Vitamin A** is essential for healthy vision, cell growth and a strong immune system. Load up on dairy products, meat (particularly liver), fish (especially mackerel and salmon), eggs, carrots and leafy green veg.

- **Vitamin C** is found in oranges, strawberries, kiwi fruit, bell peppers and leafy green vegetables. It's fantastic for strengthening our bodies' defences, as well as lowering our risk of high blood pressure and heart disease.

- **Vitamin D** helps your teeth and bones stay in tip-top shape. Soak it up naturally via sunlight or by eating salmon, sardines, egg yolks, and fortified milks and cereals.

- **Vitamin E** can help to protect our cells from damage and is also an antioxidant. Roasted sunflower seeds, spinach, kale, broccoli, mangoes and tomatoes are all good sources of vitamin E.

- **Iron** fuels the production of red blood cells, which are essential for carrying oxygen around our bodies. The best food sources are shellfish, red meat (especially liver), legumes (beans, lentils, chickpeas), pumpkin seeds and broccoli.

BEGONE, SLEEP THIEF!

If you've managed to kick the alcohol habit, you can kiss goodbye to restless nights, too. But your body can take a little time to get used to the idea, which means for a short time you may still feel as though you're not getting enough sleep. Give yourself the best possible chance to get into good sleep habits by trying the following:

- Get up at the same time every day – try not to lie in at the weekend.
- Avoid catnapping during the day – especially in the early evening.
- Avoid stimulants like caffeine and smoking in the evening.
- Exercise during the day – outside, if possible, as fresh air helps us to unwind.
- If something is worrying you, write it down. Emptying our thoughts onto the page can help us process anxiety.

LET THE HERBS GIVE YOU A HAND

Many herbs can help to cleanse and support our bodies while we're adjusting to our new alcohol-free state. You could try the following holistic remedies:

- **Milk thistle** helps to support the liver in eliminating toxins.
- **Apple cider vinegar** helps to cleanse the blood and increases digestive functions, which are crucial for flushing toxins out of the body.
- **Ginseng** is a common herbal remedy that can help with feelings of depression, anxiety and fatigue.
- **Ginkgo biloba** helps to improve circulation and heart health by increasing blood flow.
- **St John's wort** can help with depression and anxiety, but can also have a counterproductive effect on other medications – always check its suitability for you with a medical professional first.

You should always consult your doctor or a pharmacist before taking herbal supplements, particularly if you are on any other type of medication.

WRITE DOWN WHY YOU'RE WONDERFUL

Writing a list of what we think our good points are can be a useful motivator when we're finding the journey hard going. Make a list of all the things you've achieved and are proud of in life, and what helped you to reach those goals. Draw on those qualities again to fulfil your current goals. When you're feeling the tug of a glass of wine, have a look at the list and remind yourself of what you can achieve when you set your mind to it. You'll feel more determined to continue on the right path and if you're having a wobble it'll give your confidence a boost.

GIVE UP THE GUILT

You've come this far, so don't look back now. Your days of drinking may have caused you to make some questionable decisions – or worse, behave badly towards people you care about. Whatever feelings you have about your pre-sober self, it's time to let that person go – along with any shame or guilt. Those feelings don't belong in your life any more. It's not about denying who you once were or what you did, but a celebration of who you are now and how far you've travelled. Carrying around a ton of baggage is exhausting and will almost certainly lead you down the rocky road of depression and anxiety, which leaves you vulnerable to the temptations of alcohol again. Let go of the negative feelings and keep your eyes on the road ahead.

BE LUCKY

Professor Richard Wiseman's research into the concept of luck concluded that people who consider themselves lucky create their own luck by creating more positive opportunities for themselves. So, if you think yourself lucky in life, you'll become luckier as a natural consequence. In other words – you are in charge of your own fate. This is important when we're finding it hard to keep going, because only we can create the life we want to live – a life that doesn't involve alcohol. You just have to dig deep, let go of helplessness and learn to rely on yourself. But, most importantly, start looking on the bright side of life – it'll help you stay upbeat, and when you're not blaming the tough times on "bad luck", you're more likely to find ways to improve things for yourself.

FLIP YOUR THINKING

Life isn't black and white: it's all the colours of the rainbow and hundreds of shades in between. Try to avoid all-or-nothing thinking such as "I should be doing this...", "I can't do that..." or "I must stay sober" – it only leads to guilt and anxiety. Instead, try framing your thoughts in different terms – "I would like it if I stopped drinking because I know it's a positive thing to do" or "It would be great to achieve my sober milestone". Try not to play the blame game with yourself if something doesn't work out. Flip a negative situation into a positive experience. Say to yourself, "I can see what went wrong but that helps me to know what I should do differently next time." Learn from previous mistakes – it's the only way to move forward.

FIGHT THE FEAR

What if I give up? What if I can't stop cravings? What will I do if crazy Kelly invites me out and I can't say no? It's easy to let fear-based thoughts hold us back. Fear was useful for our ancestors because it stopped them getting eaten by sabre-toothed tigers. As an emotion it's vital for survival in scary life-or-death situations. It's hardwired into us. But fear is *unhelpful* when we lose perspective on it and it stops us from getting on with life and achieving our goals.

To help dispel your fears, write them down and explain why they make you afraid. Then rationalize them – pull them apart and state why they aren't true. Reference past experiences where you've confronted fear and conquered it. You've done it before – you can do it again!

LET TED GIVE YOU SOME TIPS

If you haven't heard of TED Talks then you must have been living under a stone for the past decade. Short for Technology, Entertainment and Design – although they now cover just about every topic under the sun – these short, powerful talks are like a motivational shot in the arm.

If you're flagging and you need a nudge in the right direction, try searching their talks archive for topics such as staying focused, leading a happy life, applying motivational tips and embracing a positive outlook. Many of the speakers draw on their own life experiences, making the talks even more authentic and inspirational. There are years of talks available so whatever you're looking for, you're likely to find it online at www.ted.com/talks.

KEEP AN OPEN AND CURIOUS MIND

The King of Cosmology himself, Stephen Hawking, once said: "Look up at the stars and not down at your feet. Try to make sense of what you see and wonder about what makes the universe exist. Be curious."

Keeping an open mind allows us to consider other ways of achieving our goals. Be curious about new research into living a healthier life. Think about using new technology to make your sober journey easier, such as an app or an online programme. Question your own beliefs, ideas and assumptions – is there a better way of achieving your goals? Are you doing it for the right reasons? Your journey to living alcohol-free is just one of many journeys you'll make during your lifetime. But they all share one thing in common – the will to succeed, and that can only come from you.

ALCOHOL-FREE OPTIONS AND RECIPES

Let's be honest, alcohol-free drinks used to be a bit, well, *laughable*. But times are changing and so is the trend for alcohol-free beverages. The new market for non-alcoholic spirits saw sales increase by an enormous 418 per cent in the UK in 2018–19, and we're not just turning to fizzy drinks to get a fix either. Instead, we're choosing natural ingredients like fresh fruit and berries, and blending them into smoothies and cordials. Yum-yum.

Get ready to ditch the aspirin and say hello to ten totally tasty alcohol-free options.

"PRETTY AS A PEACH" COOLER

Makes approximately 1.5 litres

A blend of citrus flavours for ultimate refreshment – this drink is the perfect accompaniment for a summer garden party or barbecue.

Ingredients: Juice of 2 lemons · Juice of 2 limes · 1 lemon, thinly sliced · 1 lime, thinly sliced · 500 ml peach nectar · 750 ml cloudy lemonade · A handful of strawberries, sliced · 250 ml sparkling water · A few springs of mint

Put the juice of the lemons and limes into a large jug. Add a handful of ice and the sliced lemon and lime. Fill the jug to one-third full with peach nectar, then fill almost to the top with cloudy lemonade. Add the sliced strawberries and top up the jug with sparkling water. Garnish with the sprigs of mint.

VERY BERRY SMOOTHIE

Quantities can be adapted depending on your blender size; the recipe below makes enough for 1–2 servings.

Delicious as an alternative to breakfast, this smoothie has everything you need to start your day the right way.

Ingredients: 250 g frozen berries of your choice • 1 banana, sliced • 250 g low-fat plain yogurt or berry-flavoured yogurt

Easy! Throw all the ingredients into a blender, hit the button, pour into a tumbler and enjoy. It's as simple as that.

"PUNCH BUT-NOT-DRUNK"

Makes approximately 1.5 litres

Full of zesty flavours, this alcohol-free punch is a perfect pick-me-up for your palate.

Ingredients: 100 g cranberries • 100 ml cranberry juice • 500 ml blood orange juice • Juice of 1 lime • 1 small orange and 1 lime, cut into wedges • Sprigs of mint • 600 ml sparkling apple juice

Put the cranberries in a freezer-proof container and cover with 2.5 cm of water. Pop in the freezer until solid. Mix the cranberry, blood orange and lime juices in a jug. To serve, shatter the iced cranberries from the container and drop them into a highball glass. Drop in the orange and lime wedges and some sprigs of mint. Pour in the juice from the jug and top up with the sparkling apple juice.

SOPHISTICATED SLUSHY

Makes approximately 1.5 litres

Slushies have grown up and become socially acceptable – hurrah! And not a blue tongue or any artificial colouring in sight...

Ingredients: 600 g frozen raspberries or mixed berries • Juice of 3 lemons • 225 ml soda water • 200 g crushed ice, or 10 ice cubes • 3 tbsp agave syrup or runny honey

Grab a blender or food processor and bung all the ingredients in. Blitz until the contents reach your desired slushy consistency. Serve in jars to really bring your slushy into the twenty-first century.

"A TASTE OF THE TROPICS" ICED TEA

Makes approximately 900 ml

Quench your thirst with a tropical twist on iced tea.

Ingredients: 1 mango, peeled, de-stoned and chopped • 400 ml water • 500 ml boiling water • 100 g granulated sugar • 4 tsp green tea leaves • A handful of fresh mint • 1 lime, sliced • Ice

Put half the mango in a saucepan with the sugar and 100 ml water. Heat for 8–10 minutes before straining through a sieve and leaving to cool. Pour 500 ml boiling water into a heatproof jug and add the green tea leaves. Leave to infuse for 5 minutes, then strain into a large glass jug and add a further 300 ml cold water. Put in the fridge and, when chilled, pour in the strained mango mixture, along with the remaining chopped mango, mint and lime slices. Add the ice and stir. Serve in highball glasses.

NON-ALCOHOLIC SPIRITS

If you fancy a mixed drink but minus the booze, look no further than non-alcoholic spirits. The trend for alcohol-free drinks has meant these booze-free beauties are available to buy online, and in many supermarkets and shops, meaning we can enjoy them at home. The range of options has expanded hugely in the past few years, and alongside the original non-alcoholic gins you can now buy liquor alternatives such as rum, vermouth and Campari – although some can be a little heavy on the sugar, so may not be suitable if you're on a health kick. Some options are completely original flavours, while others have mirrored the traditional tastes found in alcoholic spirits – but most importantly, all happily sit alongside your favourite mixer or can be included in a mocktail recipe without compromising on taste. Sober drinking sorted.

NON-ALCOHOLIC WINE

If wine is your go-to drink at the end of the day, non-alcoholic wine could be a game-changer. You will gain all the benefits of a sober lifestyle – research has also shown that moderate consumption of non-alcoholic red wine is better at reducing blood pressure and cholesterol than alcoholic red wine. So, if you're keen on the red stuff for "medicinal" purposes, you could do a lot worse than switching to an alcohol-free alternative. A growing market also means better quality, more flavours and a bigger range of options, meaning we can enjoy all the benefits and none of the risks of alcohol. What's not to like?

NON-ALCOHOLIC BEER

In 2020 the global non-alcoholic beer market was valued at roughly £13 billion ($18 billion), and over the coming years it is expected to grow by a compound rate of 7.5 per cent annually, reaching a value of £18 billion ($25 billion) by 2024. The good news for us is that big business equals better booze-free choices and a competitive market. What's exciting is that well-known alcoholic beer brands are getting in on the act, too, which means they're bringing out some great-tasting options. Many have zesty, citrus flavours with a hint of bitterness – a perfect companion for a lazy summer afternoon, but without the calorific content of regular beer. Bottoms up!

MOCKTAILS

No party is complete without a mocktail.

Wait... what?

Yup. It's time to stop letting cocktails have all the fun. Mocktails are here to stay, and they look just as good with a tiny umbrella and slice of lemon as their alcoholic counterparts. Mocktails are, quite simply, cocktails without the alcohol. Instead, the flavour comes from getting the balance of fruit juices, soda or infused water, and sometimes non-alcoholic spirits, exactly right. These days, mocktails have all the sophistication of a cocktail but none of the nasty side-effects. In fact, many bars and restaurants now have a dedicated mocktail menu, with options that are substantially cheaper than their boozy equivalents. The fun doesn't stop there, either – there are numerous websites and books dedicated to mixing your own mocktails, or you can try out one of the recipes listed in this chapter.

 # WONDERFUL WATER

A lack of the clear stuff can leave us flagging, but the great news is that colourless doesn't need to mean flavourless. Try these mouth-*watering* options out for size...

- **Do-it-yourself infusions** – Add your favourite fruit, vegetable, herbs or spices to a jug of cold water, stick it in the fridge and marvel at your infusion mastery.

- **Tea** – What's not to love about tea? If you fancy a change, green tea is great for boosting energy levels and mint tea is a brilliant tonic for your tummy.

- **Coffee** – Who says you need to be a barista to craft a good coffee? Try some unusual combinations, like an espressino – a mix of espresso, steamed milk and cocoa powder, or a kokochino – coffee with cold milk and 4 tsp of coconut syrup.

CONCLUSION

And breathe... You've given booze the boot, or you're at least thinking about it.

Kudos to you. Ditching the drink is not a decision to be sniffed at, particularly if it plays a starring role in your daily life. But the reality is, if you really, really want to – you will. It's as simple as that. Hopefully, this book has given you the encouragement you need to start or continue on your journey, as well as some solid reasons as to why we don't need alcohol to live our best lives. Sometimes we just need a nudge in the right direction.

Having read about alcohol's negative effects, perhaps you'll be inspired to try living a healthier life – one that is hangover-free and full of feel-good moments that you can appreciate with all your senses, rather than through the fog of a booze-battered brain. Perhaps it'll even give you the confidence to take on other challenges, such as gaining a new qualification or training for a marathon.

Whatever your path, know there is support – be that via friends, family or professionals. But most importantly, be kind to yourself. Good luck!

RESOURCES

To help you on your way, you'll find details of online sobriety communities on page 78 and book recommendations on page 80. In addition, here are some further sources of inspiration and support that you might find useful:

Websites

www.drinkaware.co.uk
www.nhs.uk/live-well/alcohol-support
www.alcohol.org/alcoholism/how-to-stop
www.alcoholics-anonymous.org.uk (Alcoholics Anonymous UK)
www.aa.org (Alcoholics Anonymous USA and Canada)

Podcasts

The Bubble Hour – Hosted by recovery author and blogger Jean McCarthy, this weekly podcast brings its listeners stories of hope from real people on the journey to sobriety.

Club Soda – Light-hearted sobriety chat, including alcohol-free drink recommendations, sober socializing as well as real-life recovery stories.

Love Sober – Helpful tips and advice on ditching the drink, from friendly hosts Kate and Mandy.

Recovery Elevator – Hosted by author Paul Churchill, the podcast covers a large range of topics and includes guest sobriety stories.

TED Talks

A simple way to break a bad habit

www.ted.com/talks/judson_brewer_a_simple_way_to_break_a_bad_habit

Psychiatrist Judson Brewer explains the relationship between mindfulness and addiction, and how to break bad habits.

The 1-minute secret to forming a new habit

www.ted.com/talks/christine_carter_the_1_minute_secret_to_forming_a_new_habit

Sociologist Christine Carter shares a simple step to keep you on track to achieve your goals.

How to change your behaviour for the better

www.ted.com/talks/dan_ariely_how_to_change_
your_behavior_for_the_better

Psychologist Dan Ariely explores why we make bad decisions (like drinking) and suggests a couple of strategies for doing the right thing.

Helplines

Drinkline (UK) – 0300 123 1110

Talk to FRANK (UK) – 0300 123 6600

Alcoholics Anonymous UK – 0800 91 77 650

Alcoholics Anonymous USA – (212) 870 3400

American Addiction Centers – (888) 907 7152

National Drug Helpline (USA) – 1844 289 0879

Alcohol and Drug Foundation (AUS) – 1300 85 85 84

Alcohol.org.nz (NZ) – 0800 787 797

If you're interested in finding out more about our books, find us on Facebook at Summersdale Publishers, on Twitter at @Summersdale and on Instagram at @summersdalebooks and get in touch. We'd love to hear from you!

www.summersdale.com